Sawan

1st

Activity Book

Good Habits

Don't Pluck Flowers

Age 3+

MANOJ PUBLICATIONS

Learning to Share

Tick the pictures that show the habit of sharing. Cross out the rest.

2

Colour the picture brightly.

3

Tick the pictures depicting good habits.

Good Manners

Water is precious. Save it.
Tick the pictures that show the
good habit of saving water.

Number the squares in the proper order. The sequence shows the process of cleaning one's feet.

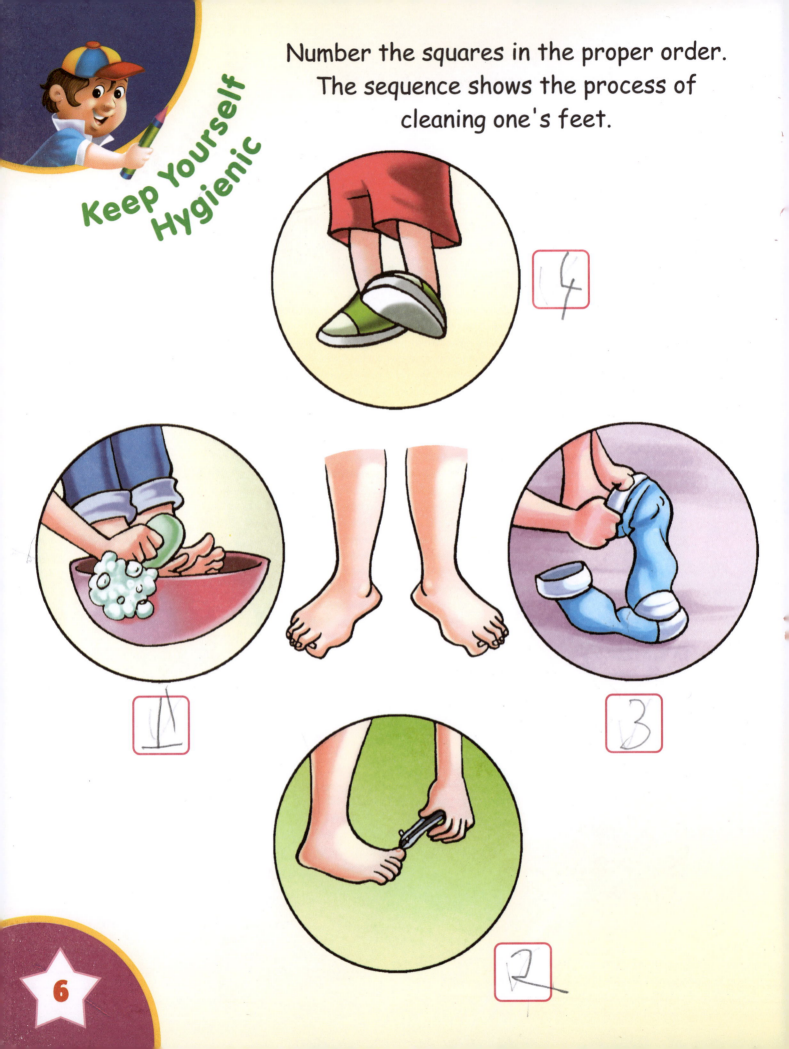

4

1

3

2

Tick the food which is good for lunch.

Circle the healthy food-options for dinner.

7

It is not healthy for kids to work all the time and play never. Let's colour the picture beautifully.

Playing is Fun!

Let's learn to take care of environment. Tick all the good habits. Colour the circle of the bad habits black.

Respect Environment

9

Oh no, it is such a dirty beach! Let's try to make a clean beach.

Redraw a clean beach in the second box.

Tick the good habits and cross out the bad habits.

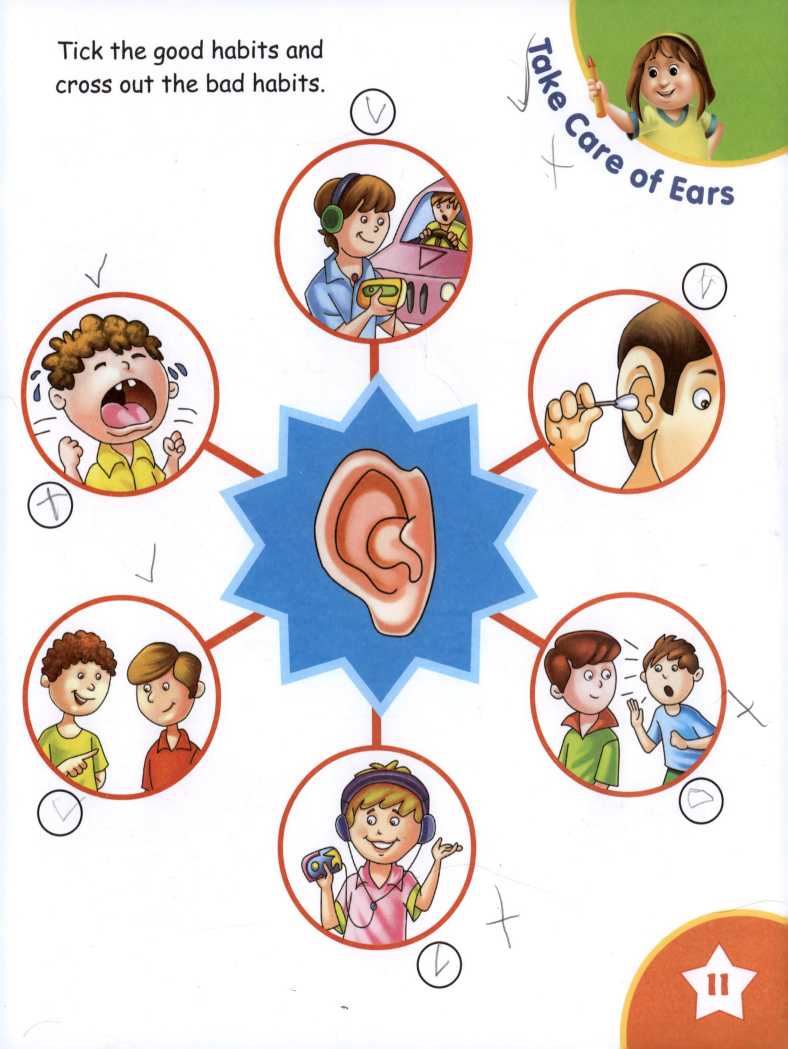

Take Care of Ears

Healthy Eating

Junk foods are bad for our health.
Circle the junk foods.

Peas

Banana

Pizza

Apple

Ice cream

Carrot

Burger

12

Here are the things that help us keep our room clean. Join them to the boxes mentioning their correct usage.

Dustbin

Dust the room.

Disinfect the floor.

Throw used paper in it.

Phenyl

Mop the floor.

13

Reading is a good habit. It helps to increase our vocabulary.
Tick the two pictures that look alike.

Put the pictures in the correct sequence.
Let's start with a hint: **Get up early...**

3

4

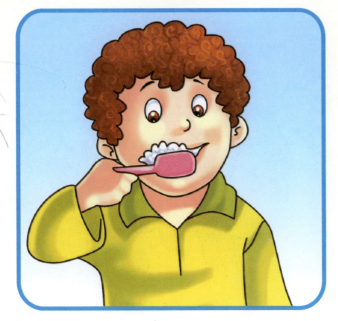

2

1

15

Tick the picture that shows a good habit.

There is a good habit in column 'B' and its respective bad habit in column 'A'. Join the two opposites together.

Traffic Rules

Column A

Column B

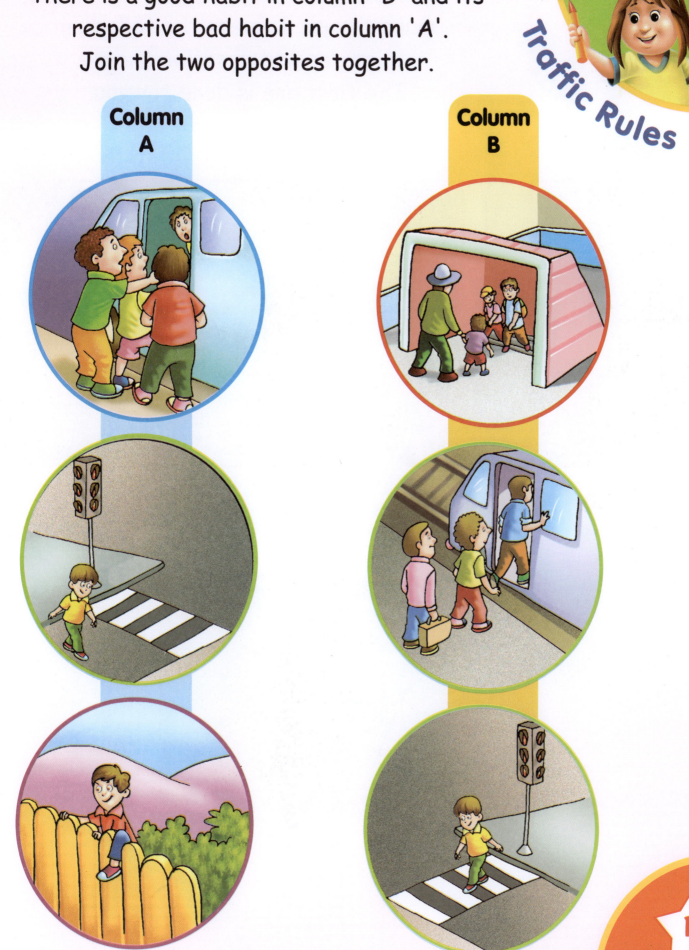

17

It is a good habit to speak softly and not to make a noise. Look at the following pictures and describe them.
The first one is done for you.

IN A LIBRARY

_____

_____

_____

Connect the dots and complete the picture.
We should listen to our teachers attentively.

Colour the boxes, that depict good habits, green.

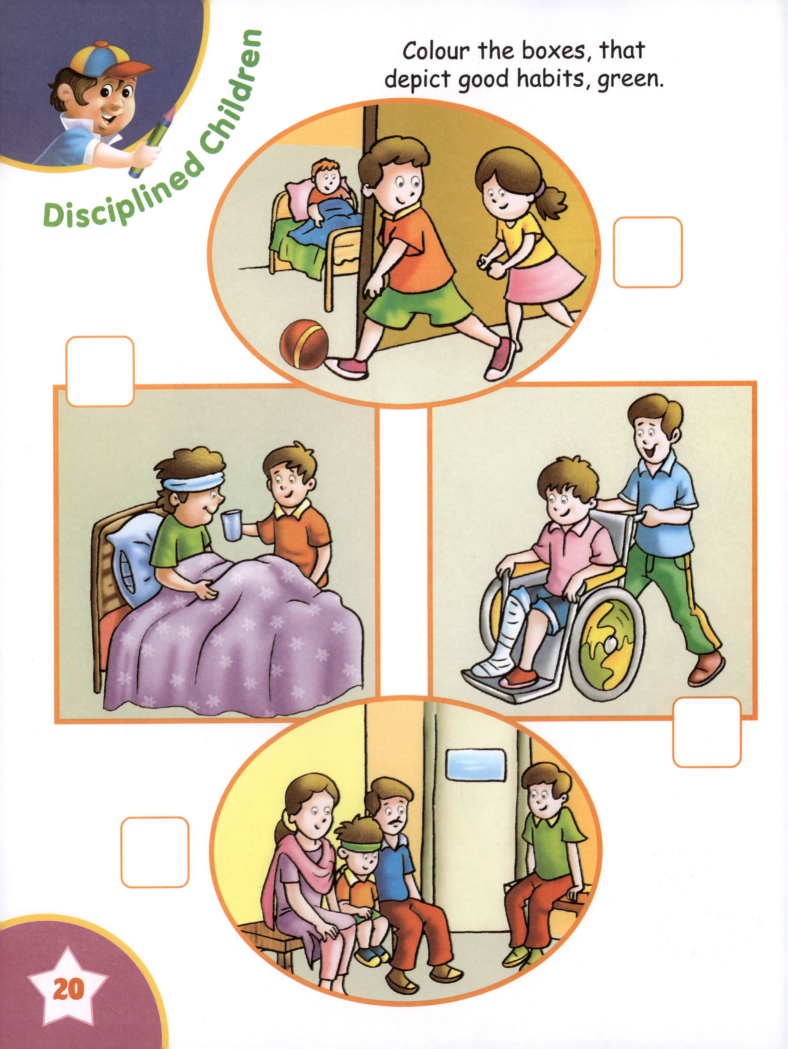

We should preserve our country's monuments and heritage. Look at the pictures and colour the correct boxes.

Admiring

Do   Don't

Scribbling damages buildings

Do   Don't

Litter in the complex

Do   Don't

Educate children about the importance of monuments

Do   Don't

Keep Smiling

(A)

(B)

Make the picture look colourful and beautiful.
Children should take care of the environment.